A Dovetale Press Adaptation

A Christmas Carol

Charles Dickens

Adaptation by
Dr Gillian Claridge
Dr B. Sally Rimkeit

Illustrations by

Fred Barnard
Reginald Birch
John Leech
Arthur Rackham
George Alfred Williams

A Dovetale Press Adaptation
A Christmas Carol
Charles Dickens

Adapted by Dr Gillian Claridge and Dr B. Sally Rimkeit
Copyright 2016 © Gillian Claridge and B. Sally Rimkeit

This edition published by Dovetale Press 2016

National Library of New Zealand Cataloguing-in-Publication Data:
Claridge, Gillian.
A Dovetale Press adaptation, A Christmas Carol Charles Dickens/
adaptation by Dr Gillian Claridge and Dr B. Sally Rimkeit. Second edition.
ISBN 978-0-473-37294-1.
I. Rimkeit, B. Sally, 1958- II. Dickens, Charles, 1812-1870.
Christmas Carol.
III. Title.
NZ823.3—dc 23

Comments and questions, please email: editor@dovetalepress.com

All titles in this Dovetale Press series are carefully constructed to enhance readability. Our other titles are
A Dovetale Press Adaptation of Little Women by Louisa May Alcott
ISBN 978-0-473-37295-8
A Dovetale Press Adaptation of The Garden Party & The Doll's House
by Katherine Mansfield ISBN 978-0-473-37291-0
A Dovetale Press Adaptation of Sherlock Holmes: The Adventure of the
Blue Carbuncle by Arthur Conan Doyle ISBN 978-0-473-37293-4
A Dovetale Press Selection: Poetry for the Restless Heart
ISBN 978-0-473-37292-7

Arthur Rackham 1915

STAVES

Marley's Ghost.

Marley was dead: to begin with. There is no doubt whatever about that. The register of his burial was signed by the clergyman, the clerk, the undertaker, and the chief mourner. Scrooge signed it: and Scrooge's name was good for anything he chose to put his hand to. Scrooge's partner, old Marley, was as dead as a door-nail.

Mind! I don't mean to say that I know, of my own knowledge, what there is particularly dead about a door-nail. I might have been inclined, myself, to regard a coffin-nail as the deadest piece of iron mongery in the trade. But the wisdom of our ancestors is in the simile; and my unhallowed hands shall not disturb it, or the Country's done for.

You will therefore permit me to repeat, emphatically, that Marley was as dead as a door-nail.

Scrooge never painted out Old Marley's name above the warehouse door. The firm was known as Scrooge and Marley. Scrooge answered to both names: it was all the same to him.

Oh! But he was a tight-fisted hand at the grindstone, that Scrooge! A squeezing, wrenching, grasping, scraping, clutching, covetous old sinner! He carried his own low temperature always about with him and didn't thaw it one degree at Christmas.

Nobody ever stopped Scrooge in the street to say, with gladsome looks, "My dear Scrooge, how are you? When will you come to see me?" But what did he care? It was the very thing he liked.

Once upon a time, of all the good days in the year, on Christmas Eve, old Scrooge sat busy in his counting-house. It was cold, bleak, biting, foggy weather. The city clocks had only just gone three, but it was quite dark already: it had not been light all day.

Scrooge had a very small fire, and his clerk had one that was so very much smaller that it looked like one coal.

"A Merry Christmas, Uncle! God save you!" cried the cheerful voice of Scrooge's nephew from the door. He came in all aglow, his eyes sparkling.

"A Merry Christmas, uncle! God save you!" cried a cheerful voice.

"Bah!" said Scrooge, "Humbug! Merry Christmas? What right have you to be merry? You're poor enough. What's Christmas time to you but a time for paying bills without money? Every idiot who goes about with 'Merry Christmas,' on his lips, should be boiled with his own pudding, and buried with a stake of holly through his heart!"

"Don't be angry, Uncle. Come! Dine with us tomorrow," said the nephew.

"Bah humbug!" cried Scrooge, "Good afternoon, Sir!"

As Scrooge's nephew went out, two gentlemen came in, collecting for the poor and destitute.

One of the gentlemen explained, "A few of us are endeavouring to raise a fund to buy the Poor some meat and drink, and means of warmth. We choose this time, because it is a time, of all others, when Want is keenly felt, and Abundance rejoices. What shall I put you down for?"

"Nothing!" Scrooge replied.

Seeing clearly that it would be useless to pursue their point, the gentlemen withdrew.

Meanwhile the fog and darkness thickened. The cold became intense. The brightness of the shops, where holly sprigs and berries crackled in the lamp-heat of the windows, made pale faces ruddy as they passed.

Poulterers' and grocers' trades became a splendid joke at Christmastime: a glorious pageant, with which it was impossible to believe that such dull principles as bargain and sale had anything to do.

At length the hour of shutting up the counting-house arrived. Scrooge turned to his clerk Bob Cratchit, "You'll want all day off tomorrow, I suppose?" said he.

"If quite convenient, Sir," said the clerk.

"It's not convenient," said Scrooge, "and it's not fair. If I was to stop half-a-crown for it, you'd think yourself ill used, I'll be bound? But I suppose you must have the whole day. Be here all the earlier next morning!"

Scrooge took his melancholy dinner in his usual melancholy tavern. Having read all the news-papers, and beguiled the rest of the evening with his banker's book, he went home to his melancholy chambers.

As Scrooge put the key in the lock of the door, he saw in the knocker, without its undergoing any intermediate process of change, not a knocker, but the face of old Marley, his dead partner.

Scrooge looked fixedly at this phenomenon and it was a knocker again.

To say that Scrooge was not startled would be untrue. But he put his hand upon the key he had relinquished, turned it sturdily, walked in, and lighted his candle.

Scrooge then walked through his rooms to see that all was right. All as they should be. Nobody under the table, nobody under the sofa. Quite satisfied, he closed his door, and double-locked himself in.

"Humbug!" said Scrooge.

But then Scrooge heard a clanking noise, as if some person were dragging a heavy chain. The Ghost of Marley floated through the heavy door: the same face, the very same.

Marley was in his pig-tail and usual waistcoat. The chain he drew was clasped about his middle. It was made (for Scrooge observed it closely) of cashboxes, keys, padlocks, ledgers, deeds, and heavy purses wrought in steel.

"How now!" said Scrooge, caustic and cold as ever, not believing what he saw, "What do you want with me?"

"Much!" Marley's voice, no doubt about it. And the spectre shook its chain, and wrung its shadowy hands.

"You are fettered," said Scrooge, starting to tremble. "Tell me why?"

"I wear the chain I forged in life," replied the Ghost of Marley. "But do you know the weight and length of the strong coil you bear yourself, Ebenezer Scrooge? It is a ponderous chain, and I am here to-night to warn you, that you have yet a chance and hope of escaping my fate. You will be haunted by Three Spirits. Expect the first Spirit tomorrow, when the bell tolls one."

"I – I think I'd rather not," said Scrooge.

The Ghost ignored him and said, "Expect the second Spirit on the next night at the same hour. Then, the third Spirit upon the next night when the last stroke of twelve has ceased to vibrate."

Then the Ghost floated out upon the bleak, dark night and joined a multitude of phantoms, wandering hither and thither in restless haste, and moaning as they went.

Every phantom wore chains like Marley's Ghost; none were free. The misery with them all was, clearly, that they sought to interfere, for good, in human matters, and had lost the power to do so for ever.

Scrooge tried to say "Humbug!" but stopped at the first syllable, and instead went to bed and straight to sleep.

Scrooge was woken when the clock struck
one, by a strange figure, like a child: yet
not so like a child as like an old man,
diminished to a child's proportions.
It wore a tunic of the purest white,
and held a branch of fresh green holly.

"Who and what are you?" Scrooge
demanded.

"I am the Ghost of Christmas Past."

"Long past?" inquired Scrooge: observant
of its dwarfish stature.

"No. Your past. Rise! Walk with me!" said
the Ghost, and they passed through the
wall, out of the city, and stood upon an open
country road, with fields on either hand.

"Good Heavens!" said Scrooge, clasping his hands together, as he looked about him. "I was bred in this place. I was a boy here!"

They came to a school. "The school is not quite deserted," said the Ghost of Christmas Past. "A solitary child is left there still."

Scrooge said he knew it. He sobbed, for it was himself as he used to be, alone again, when all the other boys had gone home for the jolly holidays. But then the door opened and a little girl came in, clapping her tiny hands, "I have come to bring you home, dear brother!"

"Always a delicate creature, whom a breath might have withered," said the Ghost. "But she had a large heart!"

"So she had," cried Scrooge. "You're right. She was my nephew's mother."

SHE LEFT HIM, AND THEY PARTED

Then Scrooge saw himself again, but now
as a man in the prime of life. His face had
begun to wear the signs of care and avarice.
He sat by the side of a fair young girl in a
mourning-dress, in whose eyes there were
tears.

This fair girl said to the younger Scrooge,
"An idol has displaced me in your heart.
If it can cheer and comfort you in time to
come, as I would have tried to do, I have
no just cause to grieve."

"What idol has displaced you?" the younger
Scrooge rejoined.

"A golden one," she said. "I cannot live
like that, so I release you from our
contract. May you be happy in the life
you have chosen."

The Ghost then showed Scrooge the fair girl when she was married with children, but they were not his, and she was not married to him.

"Spirit!" said Scrooge in a broken voice, "Remove me from this place. I cannot bear it." And then again he found himself in his bed, and sank into a heavy sleep.

STAVE III: THE SECOND OF THE THREE SPIRITS

Awaking in the middle of a prodigiously tough snore, and sitting up in bed to get his thoughts together, Scrooge had no need to be told that the bell was again upon the stroke of one. There was no doubt that he was still in his own room, but it had undergone a surprising transformation.

Heaped up upon the floor, to form a kind of throne, were turkeys, geese, game, great joints of meat, long wreaths of sausages, mince-pies, plum-puddings, red-hot chestnuts, cherry-cheeked apples, luscious pears, immense twelfth-cakes, and seething bowls of punch, that made the chamber dim with their delicious steam.

In easy state upon this couch, there sat a jolly giant, glorious to see. "I am the Ghost of Christmas Present," said the Giant. "Look upon me!"

"Ghost," said Scrooge submissively, "conduct me where you will. I went forth last night on compulsion, and I learnt a lesson which is working now. To-night, if you have aught to teach me, let me profit by it."

"Touch my robe!"

Scrooge touched the robe of the Ghost and held it fast. The room vanished instantly, and they stood in the city streets on Christmas morning. The sky was gloomy, there was nothing very cheerful in the climate or the town, and yet was there an air of cheerfulness abroad.

This effect might have been due to the kind, generous, hearty nature of the Ghost and his sympathy with all poor men. This in turn led him to take Scrooge straight to the house of Scrooge's clerk, Bob Cratchit.

There they saw the poor Cratchit family eating Christmas dinner.

WITH THE PUDDING

Mr and Mrs Cratchit had six children, and one of them was Tiny Tim, who bore a little crutch, and had his limbs supported by an iron frame. They had scrimped and saved to buy their Christmas dinner, for Scrooge only paid Bob Cratchit fifteen shillings a week. They were very poor.

But the goose they had for dinner was universally admired. Eked out by apple-sauce and mashed potatoes, it was a sufficient dinner for the whole family. Indeed, as Mrs Cratchit said with a great delight (surveying one small atom of a bone upon the dish), they hadn't ate it all at last!

Yet, for once in the year, every one had had enough. Then Mrs Cratchit went to fetch the pudding. She entered the room, flushed but smiling proudly, with the pudding like a speckled cannon-ball, hard and firm, blazing in half-a-quart of ignited brandy and bedecked with Christmas holly stuck to the top.

Everybody had something to say about it, but nobody said or thought it was at all a small pudding for a large family. It would have been flat heresy to do so. Any Cratchit would have blushed to hint at such a thing.

And when dinner was finally done and cleared away, Bob proposed, "A Merry Christmas to us all, my dears. God bless us!" which all the family re-echoed.

"God bless us every one!" said Tiny Tim, the last of all.

"Spirit," said Scrooge, with an interest he had never felt before, "tell me if Tiny Tim will live."

"I see a vacant seat," replied the Ghost, "in the poor chimney corner, and a crutch without an owner, carefully preserved. If these shadows remain unaltered by the Future, the child will die."

"No, no," said Scrooge. "Oh no, kind Spirit!
Say Tiny Tim will be spared."

But the Ghost did not give an answer, and he and Scrooge set off again upon their travels. Much they saw, and far they went, and many homes they visited, but always with a happy end.

The Ghost stood beside sick beds and they were cheerful; on foreign lands and they were close at home; by struggling men and they were patient in their greater hope; by poverty and it was rich.

In almshouse, hospital and jail, in misery's every refuge, where vain man in his little brief authority had not made fast the door and barred the Christmas Spirit out, the Ghost left his blessing and taught Scrooge his precepts.

STAVE IV: THE LAST
OF THE SPIRITS

The Last of the Spirits.

Then the clock struck twelve and Scrooge was back once again in his gloomy rooms. There, Scrooge beheld a solemn Ghost, draped and hooded, coming like a mist along the ground towards him.

When the Ghost came near him, Scrooge bent down upon his knee. For in the very air through which this Ghost moved, it seemed to scatter gloom and mystery. Its presence filled Scrooge with a solemn dread. It spoke not a word.

"Am I in the presence of the Ghost of Christmas Yet To Come?" said Scrooge. The Spirit answered not, but pointed onward with its hand.

"Ghost of the Future!" exclaimed Scrooge, "I fear you more than any Spectre I have seen. But, as I know your promise is to do me good, lead on!"

Instantly, they were in the heart of the city amongst the merchants. The Ghost stopped beside a little knot of business men who were discussing someone who had just died, but for whom the funeral would be very cheap, as no one they knew wanted to go to it.

Scrooge could not however make out who this universally unpopular person was. He asked the Ghost: "Tell me what man that was who has just died?"

The Ghost stopped outside the window of Scrooge's office. But yet it was not his office. The furniture was not the same, and the figure in the chair was not himself. The Ghost pointed onward as before.

Scrooge joined the Ghost once again, and wondering why and whither he had gone, accompanied it until they reached an iron gate: a churchyard. Here, then, the wretched man whose name he did not know lay underneath the ground.

The Ghost stood among the graves and pointed down to one. Scrooge advanced towards it trembling and asked, "Are these the shadows of the things that Will be, or are they shadows of the things that May be, only?"

Still the Ghost pointed downward to the grave by which it stood. Scrooge crept towards it, and following the finger, read upon the stone of the neglected grave his own name, EBENEZER SCROOGE.

"Ghost," cried Scrooge, "Assure me that I
yet may change these shadows you have
shown me, by an altered life!"

But the Ghost had dwindled down into
a bedpost. Yes! And the bedpost was
Scrooge's own. The bed was his own, and
the room was his own. Best and happiest
of all, the Time before him was his own,
to make amends in!

"I don't know what
to do!" cried Scrooge,
laughing and crying in
the same breath,
"I am as light as a feather,
I am as happy as an angel.
I am as merry as a school-boy.
I am as giddy as a drunken man.
A Merry Christmas to everybody!
A Happy New Year to all the world".

"Hallo here! Whoop! Hallo! Ha ha ha!" laughed Scrooge.

Really, for a man who had been out of practice for so many years, it was a splendid laugh, a most illustrious laugh. The father of a long, long line of brilliant laughs!

Scrooge opened the window and called down to a boy in the street, "What's today?"

"Today?" replied the boy, "Why, it's Christmas Day!"

"It's Christmas Day!" exclaimed Scrooge.

"I haven't missed it! Boy, go and buy the biggest turkey you can find and tell them to bring it here. Come back with it in less than five minutes, and I'll give you half-a-crown!"

The boy was off like a shot. "I'll send it to Bob Cratchit's!" whispered Scrooge, rubbing his hands and splitting with a laugh.
"He sha'n't know who sends it. It's twice the size of Tiny Tim."

Scrooge dressed himself all in his best, and at last got out into the streets which were full of people. Scrooge regarded every one with a delighted smile.

He gave the gentlemen collecting for the poor a great deal of money. He went to church.

He looked so irresistibly pleasant, in a word, that three or four good-humoured fellows said, "Good morning, sir! A Merry Christmas to you!"

And Scrooge said often afterwards, that
of all the blithe sounds he had ever heard,
"Merry Christmas" was the blithest in
his ears.

In the afternoon, Scrooge turned his steps
to his nephew's house. He passed the door
a dozen times before he had the courage
to knock, but he made a dash and did it.
The maid showed him upstairs to the
dining room.

"Why bless my soul!" cried Fred,
"who's that?"

"It's I. Your Uncle Scrooge. I have come to
dinner. Will you let me in, Fred?"

Let him in! It is a mercy Fred didn't shake
his uncle's arm off. Scrooge felt at home in
five minutes. Nothing could be heartier.

Wonderful party, wonderful games,
wonderful unanimity, won-der-ful happiness!

Scrooge was early at the office next morning. Oh, he was early there. If he could only be there first and catch Bob Cratchit coming late! That was the thing he had set his heart upon. And he did it; yes he did! The clock struck nine. No Bob. A quarter past. No Bob. He was full eighteen minutes and a half behind his time.

"Hallo!" growled Scrooge, in his accustomed voice as near as he could feign it, when Bob arrived. "What do you mean by coming here at this time of day?"

"I'm very sorry, sir," said Bob. "I… am… behind my time."

"You are?" repeated Scrooge. "Yes. I think you are. Step this way, if you please."

"It's only once a year, sir," pleaded Bob.

"Now, I'll tell you what, my friend," said
Scrooge, "I am not going to stand this sort
of thing any longer. And therefore," he
continued, leaping from his stool, and giving
Bob such a dig in the waistcoat that he
staggered back, "and therefore I am about to
raise your salary!"

Bob trembled. He had a momentary idea of
knocking Scrooge out and calling for help
and a strait-jacket.

But Scrooge said, "A Merry Christmas,
Bob," with an earnestness that could not be
mistaken as he clapped him on the back.

"A Merrier Christmas, Bob, my good fellow,
than I have given you for many a year!

"I'll raise your salary," said Scrooge, "and endeavour to assist your struggling family. We will discuss your affairs this very afternoon, over a Christmas drink, Bob! Make up the fires, and buy another coal-scuttle before you dot another i, Bob Cratchit!"

Scrooge was better than his word. He did it all and infinitely more. And to Tiny Tim, who did NOT die, he was a second father. He became as good a friend, as good a master, and as good a man as the good old city knew.

Some people laughed to see the alteration in Scrooge, but he couldn't have cared less. Everyone always said of him that he knew how to keep Christmas well, if anyone did.

And so, as Tiny Tim observed,
"God Bless Us, Every One!"

CPSIA information can be obtained
at www.ICGtesting.com
Printed in the USA
BVHW021448311022
650754BV00005B/27